# CENTERS for EARLY NUMBERS

## by Marilynn G. Barr

# I Know All About Numbers

# I Know All About Numbers

Publisher: Monday Morning Books, Inc.

Production: Little Acorn & Associates, Inc.

MM2223
CENTERS FOR EARLY NUMBERS
Entire contents copyright © 2007
by Monday Morning Books, Inc.

For a complete catalog, write to the address below:
Monday Morning Books, Inc.
PO Box 1134
Inverness, CA 94937

Call our toll-free number: 1-800-255-6049
E-mail us at: MMBooks@aol.com
Visit our Web site: http://www.mondaymorningbooks.com
For more products featuring art by Marilynn G. Barr visit www.littleacornbooks.com

Monday Morning® and the Monday Morning sun logo are
registered trademarks of Monday Morning Books, Inc.

ISBN 1-57612-227-1

Printed in the United States of America
9 8 7 6 5 4 3 2 1

# Contents

# Introduction

*Centers for Early Numbers* offers children plenty of number skills practice. Children practice sorting and matching numerals, number sets, and number words. Youngsters also strengthen fine motor skills as they attach clothespins to match boards, trace and write numbers, and cut out and glue puppet patterns to craft sticks. Each center includes five practice stations: Match It, Trace It, Write It, Read It, and Review It. While very early learners may require some guidance as they move from station to station, each activity is designed for self-directed skills practice.

## Setting Up Centers

Below is a list of supplies and storage formats to set up each five-station center for children to practice matching, tracing, writing, reading, and reviewing. Set up an additional "Make It" station for children to make stick puppets. Children can work individually or in small groups.

### Supplies:

Construction paper, oak tag, crayons, glue, markers, scissors, file folders, craft sticks, clothespins, loose leaf binders, wipe-off crayons, paper plates (optional), baskets, file boxes

### Folders:

Decorate folders to store Trace It and Write It activities as well as mini book pages and Review It activities.

### Binders:

Fill binders with laminated activity sheets to keep in each station. Trace It, Write It, and the Number of the Day Flip Chart pages are designed with three holes to punch and place in loose leaf binders.

Reproduce, color, cut out, and tape or glue the Number of the Day Flip Chart cover to the front of a binder. Decorate oak tag covers for separate Trace It and Write It activity binders.

## Assembling Activities

### Match It

Reproduce, color, and cut out plain paper, oak tag, or poster board match boards. Laminate or glue plain paper match boards to paper plates for stability. Reproduce, color, cut out, and glue clothespins to the backs of matching cutouts.

Children clip clothespins to matching spaces around the match boards. Store Match It activities in separate resealable plastic bags. Place the bags in a basket in the designated Match It station.

### Trace It

• Reproduce and place a supply of Trace It activity sheets in separate folders. Place a basket of crayons at the Trace It station for children to practice tracing numerals and number words. Store the folders in a file box decorated with puppet cutouts.

• Trace It Binder: Decorate and glue or tape a cover to the front of a binder to hold laminated Trace It activity sheets. Reproduce, color, laminate, and place Trace It activity sheets in the binder for children to practice tracing numerals and number words. Store wipe-off crayons in a loose leaf pencil pocket in the binder.

4

## Write It

• Reproduce and place a supply of Write It activity sheets in separate folders. Place a basket of crayons at the Write It station for children to practice writing numerals and number words. Store the folders in a file box decorated with puppet cutouts.

• Write It Binder: Decorate and glue or tape a cover to the front of a binder to hold Write It activity sheets. Reproduce, color, laminate, and place Write It activity sheets in the binder for children to practice writing numerals and number words. Store wipe-off crayons in a loose leaf pencil pocket in the binder.

## Read It

Use mini book pages to make supersized and mini books for children to practice reading and learning about numbers.

• Supersized Book: Enlarge, reproduce, color, and cut out each two-page mini book. Decorate a construction paper cover for each book. (Page one of each book can be used as a cover.)

• Make and Read It: Reproduce and staple several sets of mini book pages. Place like sets in separate folders in a decorated file box in the Read It station.

Help early learners color, cut out, and assemble book pages. Place pre-cut sheets of construction paper in a basket for children to decorate covers for their mini books. Write each child's name on the back of his or her assembled book.

## Review It

Reproduce, color, and cut out each set of Review It patterns and cutouts. Matching in the center, glue each set of patterns inside a file folder. Decorate the front of the folder. Laminate the folder. Tape a construction paper pocket or an envelope to the back of each folder to store matching cutouts.

Store Review It folders in a file box in the designated station.

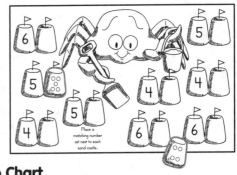

## Puppets

Reproduce and cut out puppet patterns. Place the patterns in a basket with crayons for children to color and decorate. Help children glue craft sticks to the backs of cutouts to form stick puppets. Write each child's initials on his or her puppet.

## Labels

Reproduce, color, and cut out the labels. Program and tape the labels on storage envelopes, boxes, folders, file boxes, or baskets.

## Number of the Day Flip Chart

Introduce new numbers, number words, and counting sets with a flip chart. Reproduce, color, cut out, and tape or glue the flip chart cover to the front of a loose leaf binder. Reproduce, color, and cut out several flip chart pages. Punch a hole at each dot on each page. Cut out and glue a numeral, number word, or number set picture on each page and place it in the binder. Pages can also be programmed with magazine cutouts featuring a variety of numbers, number words, and counting sets. Children learn to recognize numerals and number words and practice counting.

## Borders

Children can practice identifying the numbers, number words, and counting sets on the borders. Reproduce, color, and cut out the border patterns. Use the borders to decorate display boards, create frames, decorate folders and binders, make headbands, and more.

5

# Match Dolphin Numbers 1-3

Reproduce, color, and cut out the match board.

6

# Match Dolphin Numbers 1-3

Reproduce, color, cut out, and glue a clothespin to the back of each bottle.

7

# Dolphin's Number Tracing Board

Look at the numbers.
Trace the numbers.
Color the matching number of dolphins.

8

# Dolphin's Number Writing Board

Look at the numbers. Write the numbers. Color the picture.

1
2
3

# Dolphin's Number Adventure

Dolphin went swimming.

Dolphin saw 1 steam boat.

Dolphin's Number Adventure

Dolphin saw 1 whale.

# Dolphin's Number Adventure

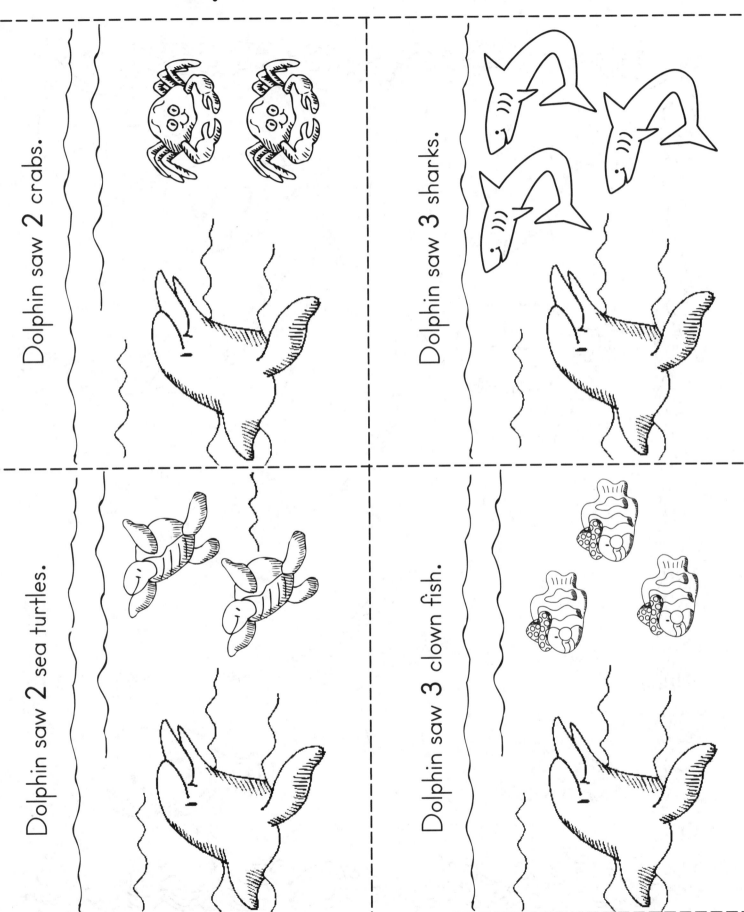

Dolphin saw 2 crabs.

Dolphin saw 3 sharks.

Dolphin saw 2 sea turtles.

Dolphin saw 3 clown fish.

11

# Match the Bottles

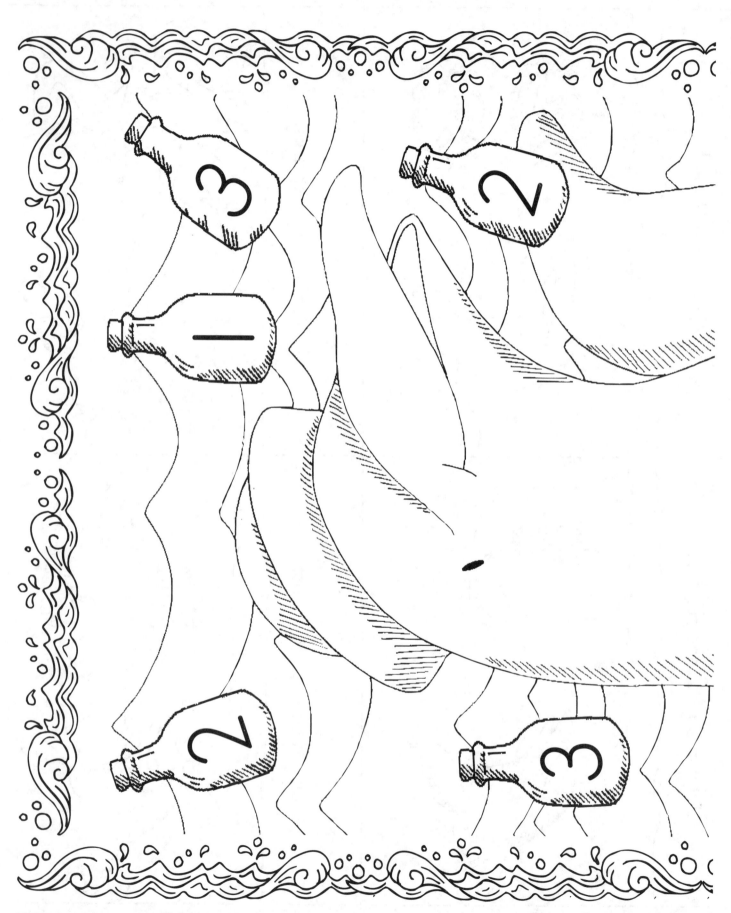

# Match the Bottles

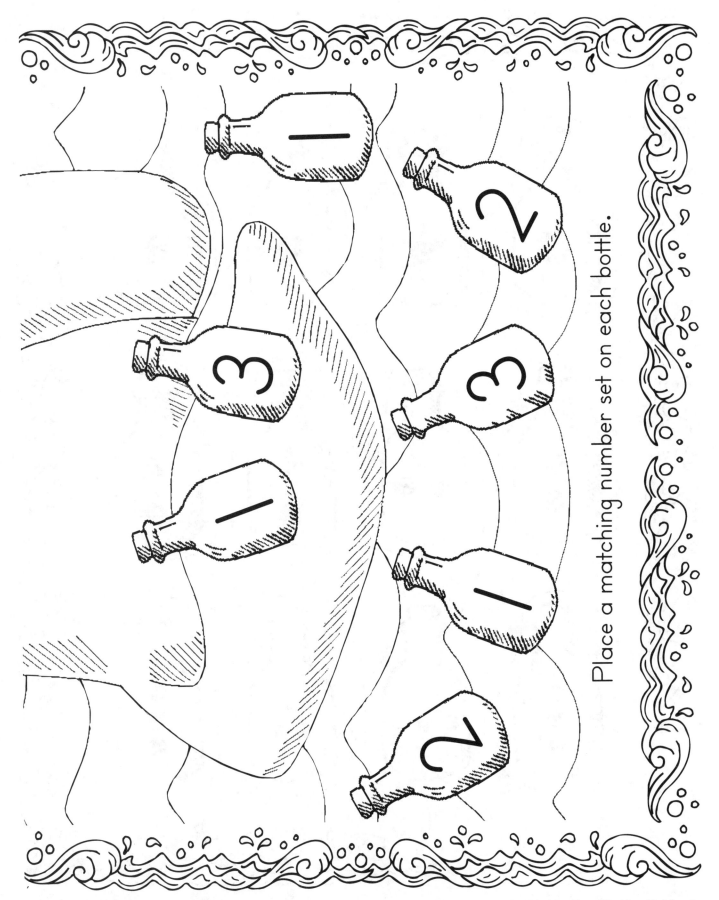

Place a matching number set on each bottle.

13

# Match the Bottles

Reproduce, color, and
cut out the bottles.

14

# Dolphin Puppets and Labels

Reproduce, color, and cut out twelve dolphin puppets. Program each dolphin with a number from one to twelve. Glue a craft stick to the back of each puppet. Place the puppets in numerical order.

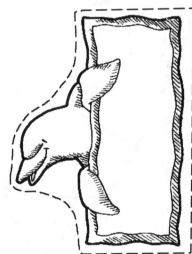

- Reproduce, color, and cut out the labels. Program and tape the labels on storage envelopes, boxes, folders, or drawers.
- Reproduce, color, and program twelve labels with numbers one to twelve. Sort and place the labels in numerical order.

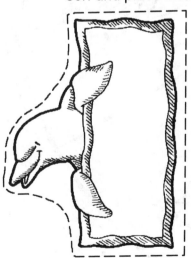 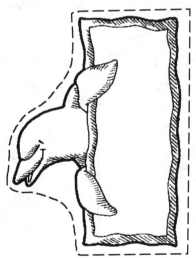

# Match Crab Numbers 4-6

Reproduce, color, and cut out the match board.

# Match Crab Numbers 4-6

Reproduce, color, cut out, and glue a clothespin to the back of each sand pail.

# Crab's Tracing Board

Look at the numbers.
Trace the numbers.
Color the matching number of crabs.

# Crab's Writing Board

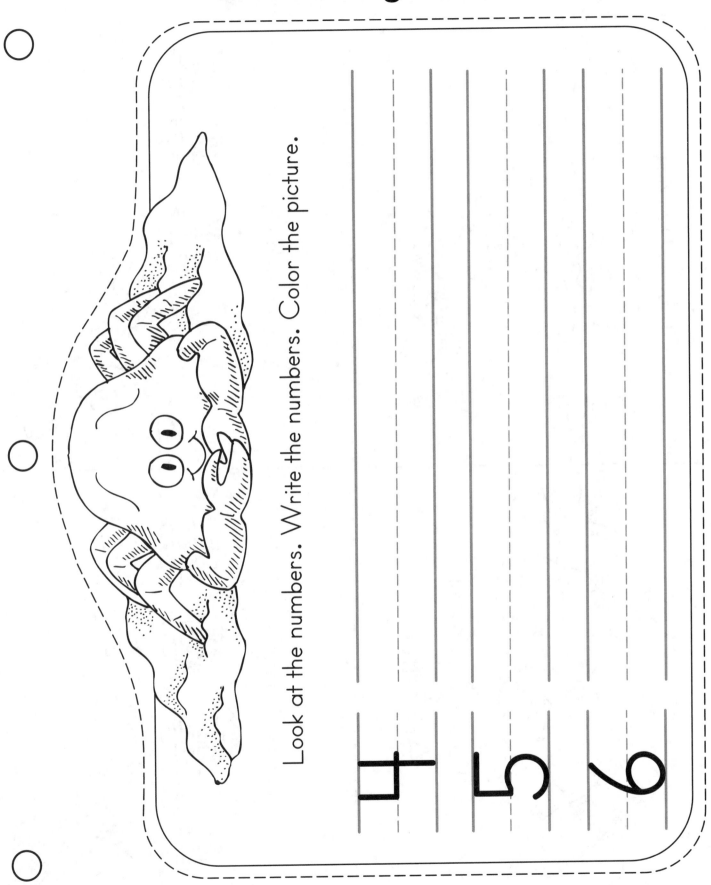

Look at the numbers. Write the numbers. Color the picture.

4
5
6

# Crab's Number Adventure

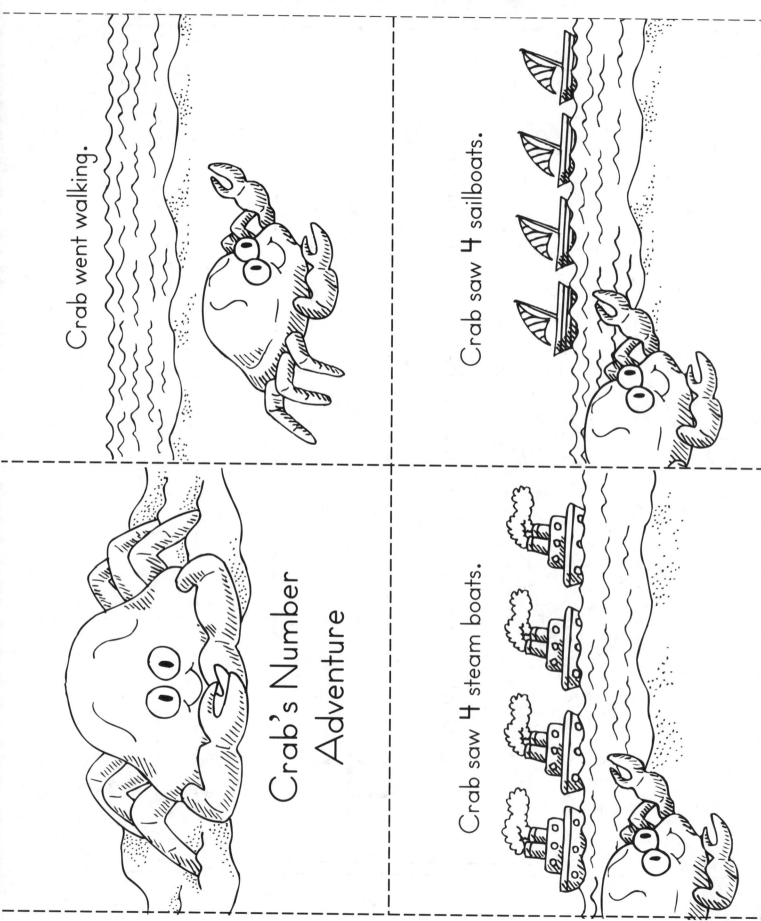

Crab went walking.

Crab's Number Adventure

Crab saw 4 sailboats.

Crab saw 4 steam boats.

# Crab's Number Adventure

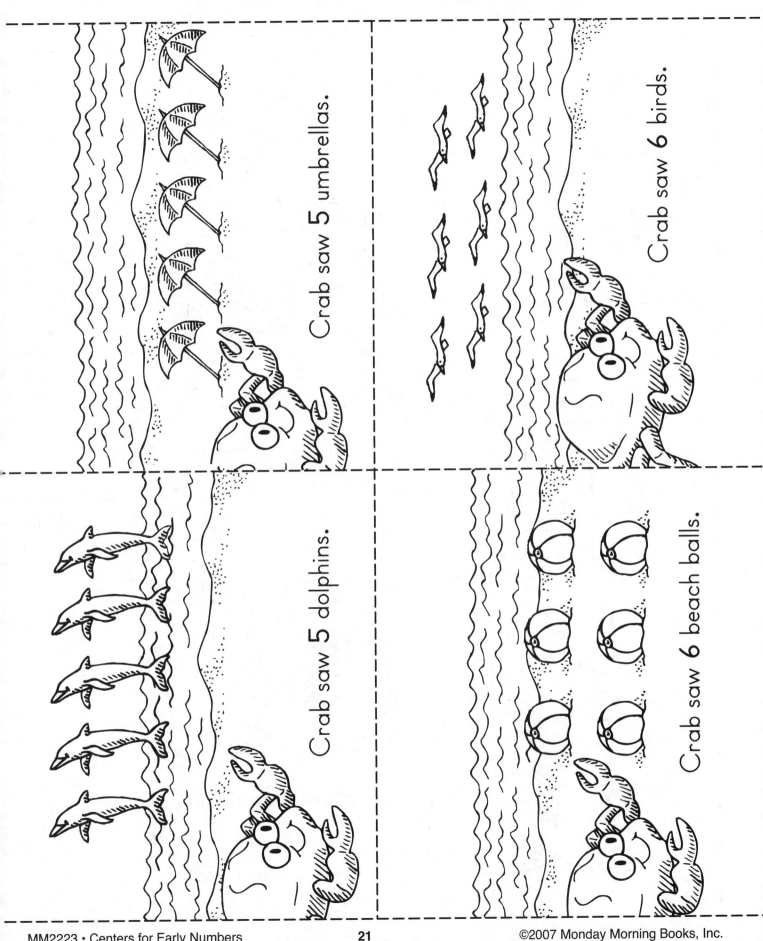

Crab saw 5 umbrellas.

Crab saw 6 birds.

Crab saw 5 dolphins.

Crab saw 6 beach balls.

# Match Crab's Sand Castles

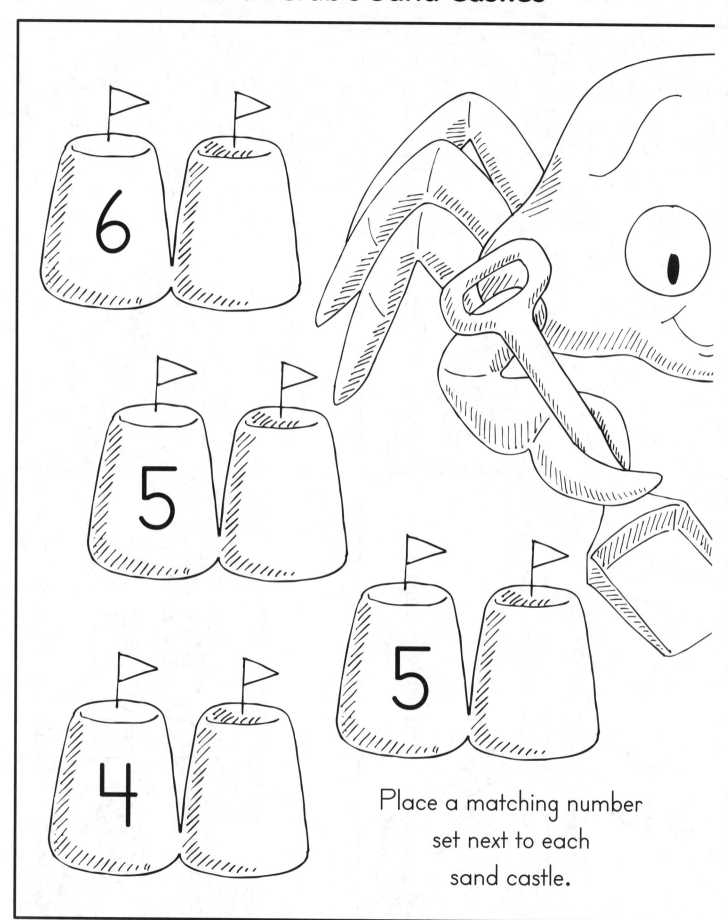

Place a matching number
set next to each
sand castle.

# Match Crab's Sand Castles

23

# Match Crab's Sand Castles

Reproduce, color, and cut out the sand castles.

24

# Crab Puppets and Labels

Reproduce, color, and cut out twelve crab puppets. Program each crab with a number from one to twelve. Glue a craft stick to the back of each puppet. Place the puppets in numerical order.

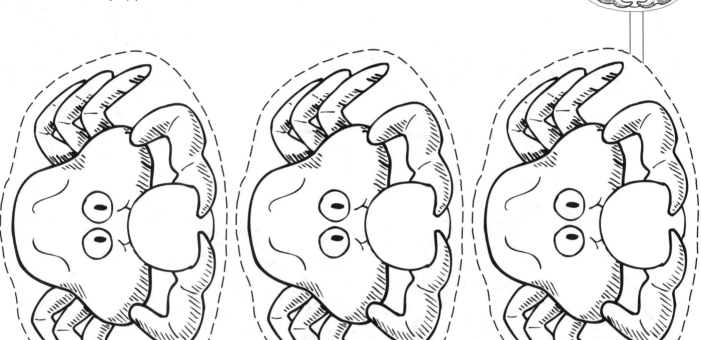

- Reproduce, color, and cut out the labels. Program and tape the labels on storage envelopes, boxes, folders, or drawers.
- Reproduce, color, and program twelve labels with numbers one to twelve. Sort and place the labels in numerical order.

# Match Sea Turtle Numbers 7-9

Reproduce, color, and cut out the match board.

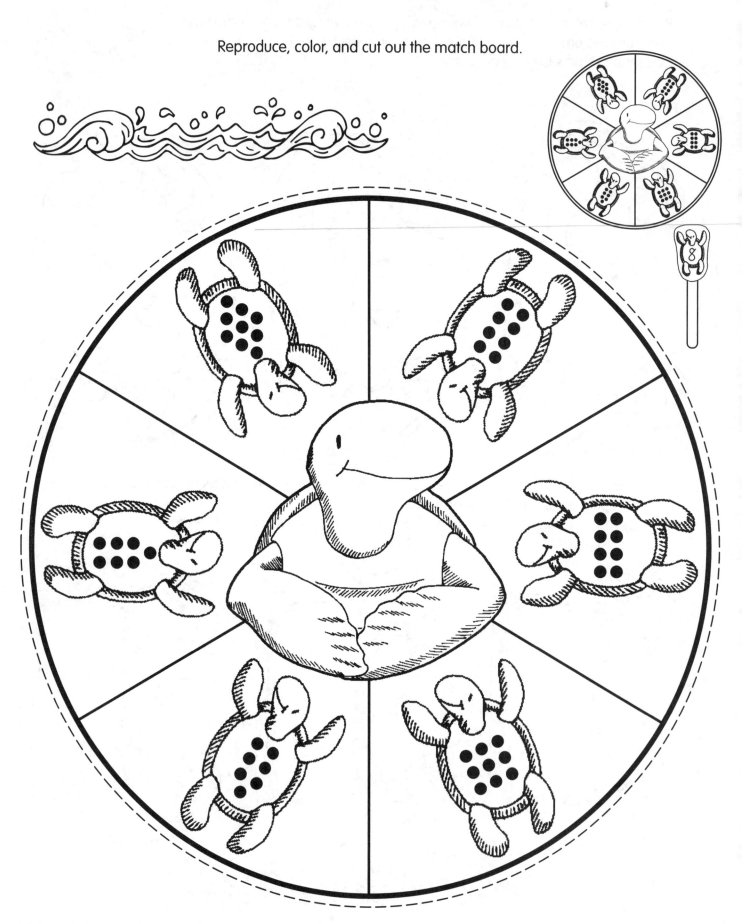

26

# Match Sea Turtle Numbers 7-9

Reproduce, color, cut out, and glue a clothespin to the back of each turtle.

# Sea Turtle's Tracing Board

Look at the numbers.
Trace the numbers.
Color the matching number of sea turtles.

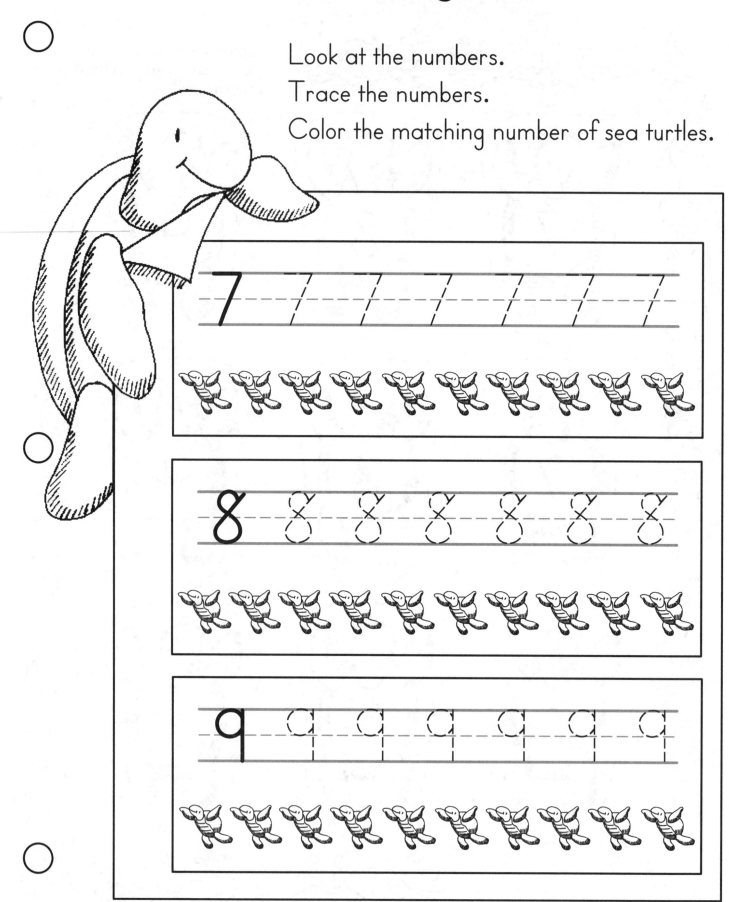

# Sea Turtle's Writing Board

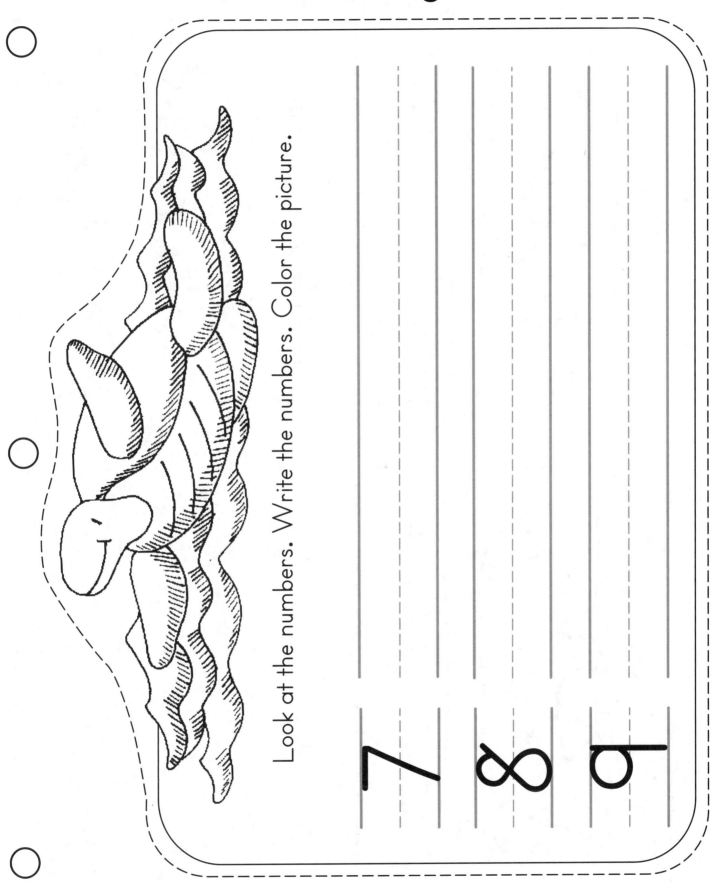

Look at the numbers. Write the numbers. Color the picture.

7

8

9

# Sea Turtle's Number Adventure

Sea Turtle went swimming.

Sea Turtle saw 7 jellyfish.

Sea Turtle's Number Adventure

Sea Turtle saw 7 clown fish.

30

# Sea Turtle's Number Adventure

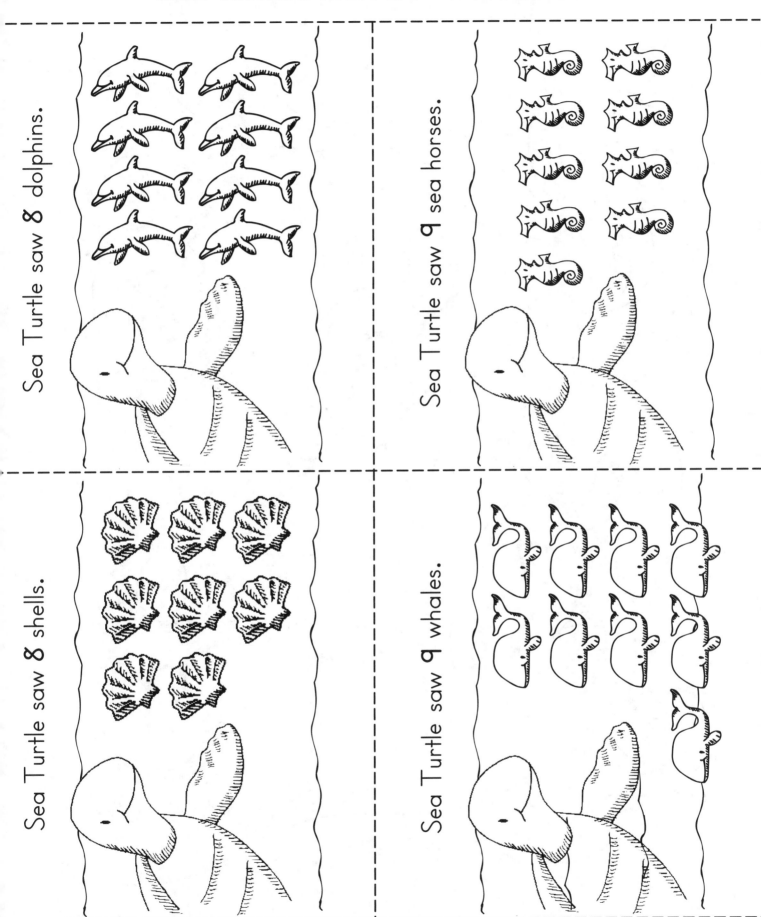

Sea Turtle saw 8 dolphins.

Sea Turtle saw 9 sea horses.

Sea Turtle saw 8 shells.

Sea Turtle saw 9 whales.

31

# Match Sea Turtles on the Beach

Place a matching number set on each sea turtle.

# Match Sea Turtles on the Beach

33

# Match Sea Turtles on the Beach

Reproduce, color, and cut out the sea turtles.

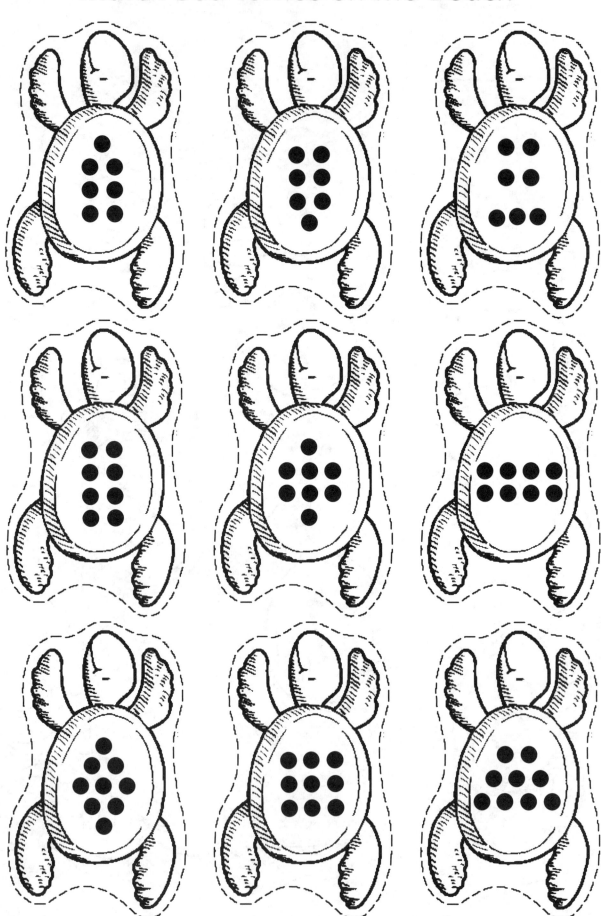

34

# Sea Turtle Puppets and Labels

Reproduce, color, and cut out twelve sea turtle puppets.
Program each sea turtle with a number from one to
twelve. Glue a craft stick to the back of each puppet.
Place the puppets in numerical order.

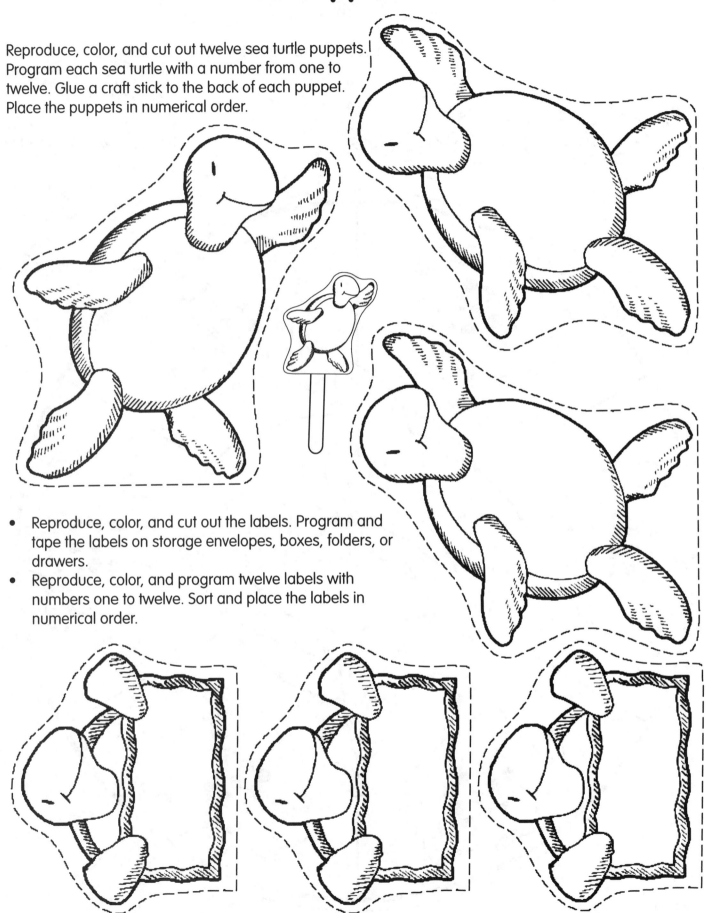

- Reproduce, color, and cut out the labels. Program and
  tape the labels on storage envelopes, boxes, folders, or
  drawers.
- Reproduce, color, and program twelve labels with
  numbers one to twelve. Sort and place the labels in
  numerical order.

35

# Match Shark Numbers 10-12

Reproduce, color, and cut out the match board.

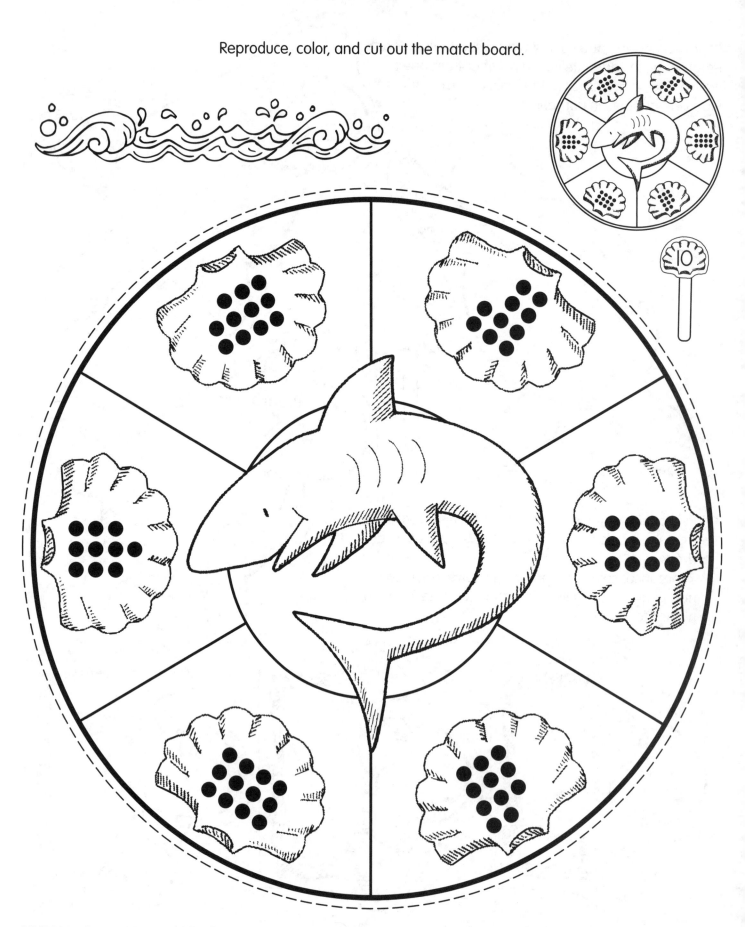

Reproduce, color, cut out, and glue a clothespin to the back of each shell.

# Shark's Tracing Board

Look at the numbers.
Trace the numbers.
Color the matching number
of sharks.

# Shark's Writing Board

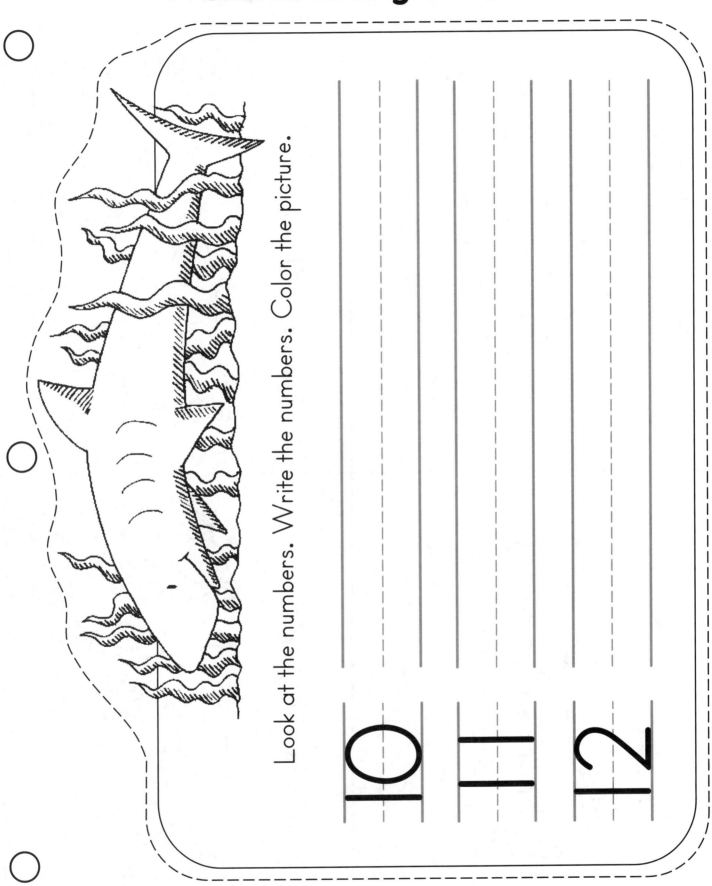

Look at the numbers. Write the numbers. Color the picture.

10

11

12

# Shark's Number Adventure

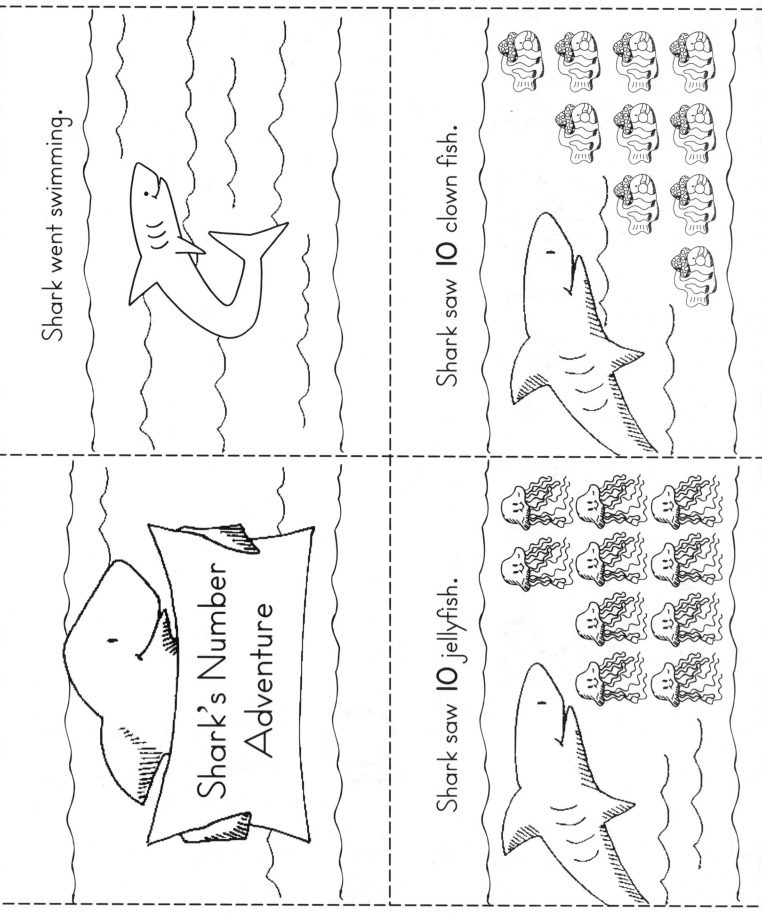

Shark went swimming.

Shark saw 10 clown fish.

Shark's Number Adventure

Shark saw 10 jellyfish.

# Shark's Number Adventure

Shark saw 11 sea turtles.

Shark saw 12 sea horses.

Shark saw 11 shells.

Shark saw 12 starfish.

41

# Match Shark's Shells

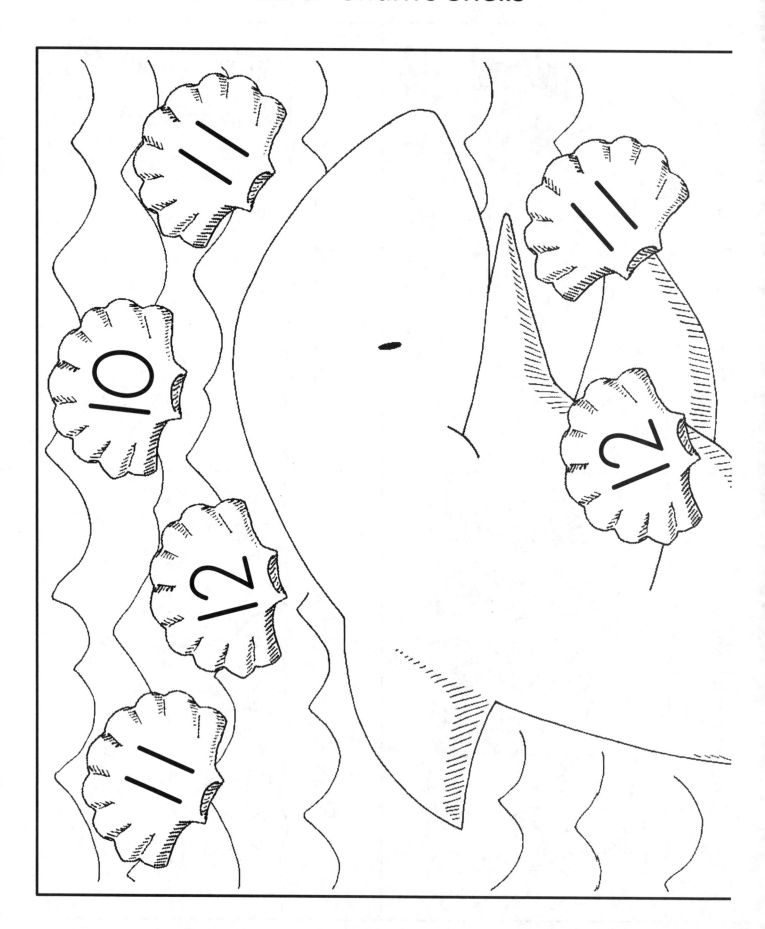

# Match Shark's Shells

Place a matching number set on each shell.

# Match Shark's Shells

Reproduce, color, and cut out the shells.

# Shark Puppets and Labels

Reproduce, color, and cut out twelve shark puppets. Program each shark with a number from one to twelve. Glue a craft stick to the back of each puppet. Place the puppets in numerical order.

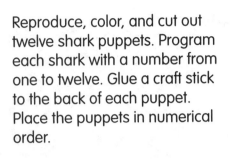

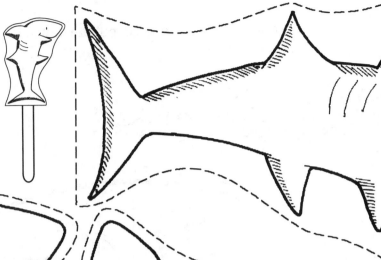

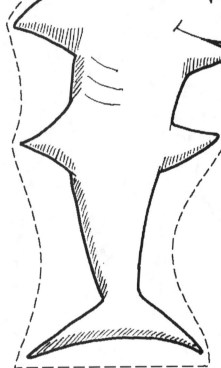

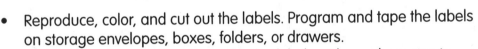

- Reproduce, color, and cut out the labels. Program and tape the labels on storage envelopes, boxes, folders, or drawers.
- Reproduce, color, and program twelve labels with numbers one to twelve. Sort and place the labels in numerical order.

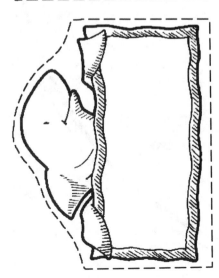
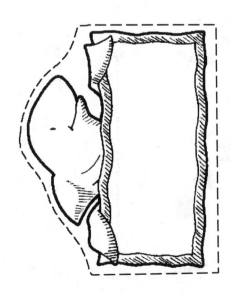
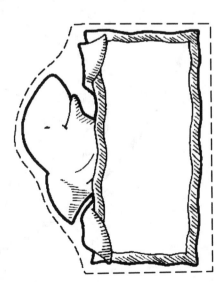

45

# Match Whale Number Words 1-3

Reproduce, color, and cut out the match board.

46

# Match Whale Number Words 1-3

Reproduce, color, cut out, and glue a clothespin to the back of each whistle.

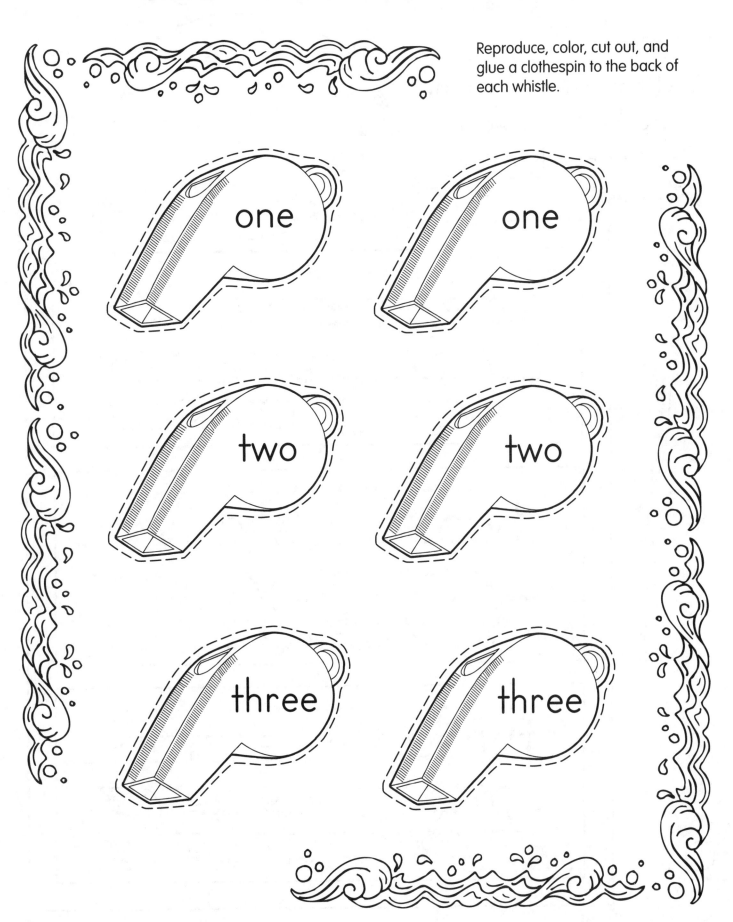

47

# Whale's Tracing Board

 Look at the number words.
Trace the number words.
Color the matching number
of whales.

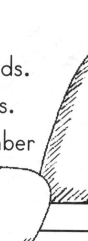

## one one one one

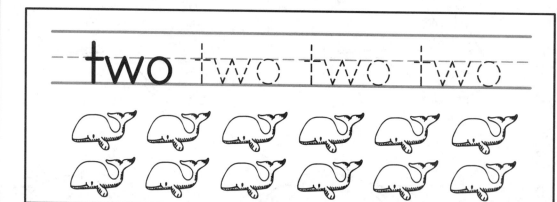

## two two two two

## three three three

48

# Whale's Writing Board

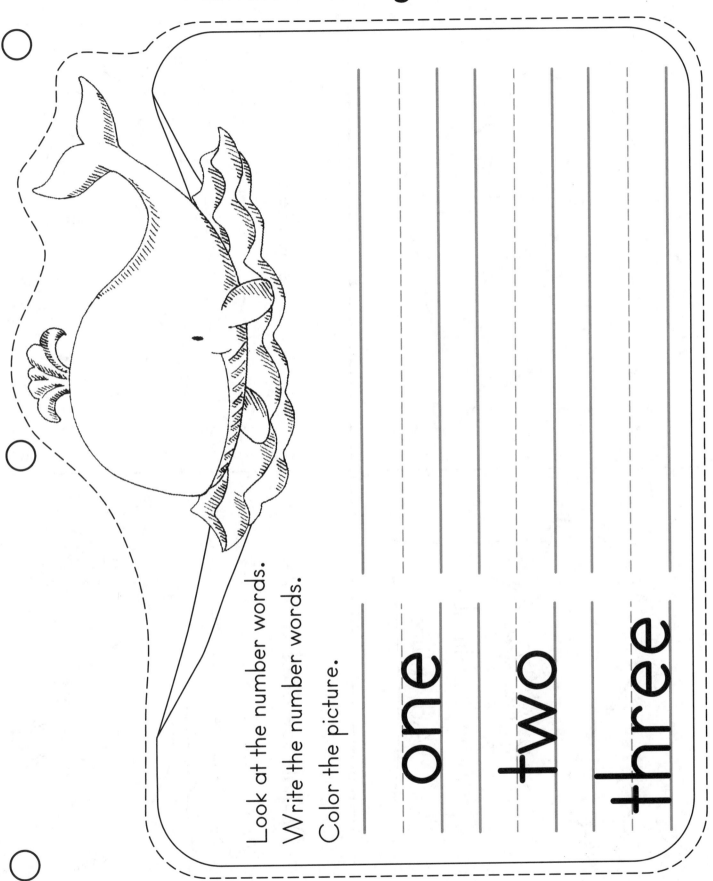

Look at the number words.
Write the number words.
Color the picture.

one

two

three

49

# Whale's Number Adventure

Whale went swimming.

Whale saw **one** shark.

Whale's Number Adventure

Whale saw **one** sea turtle.

50

# Whale's Number Adventure

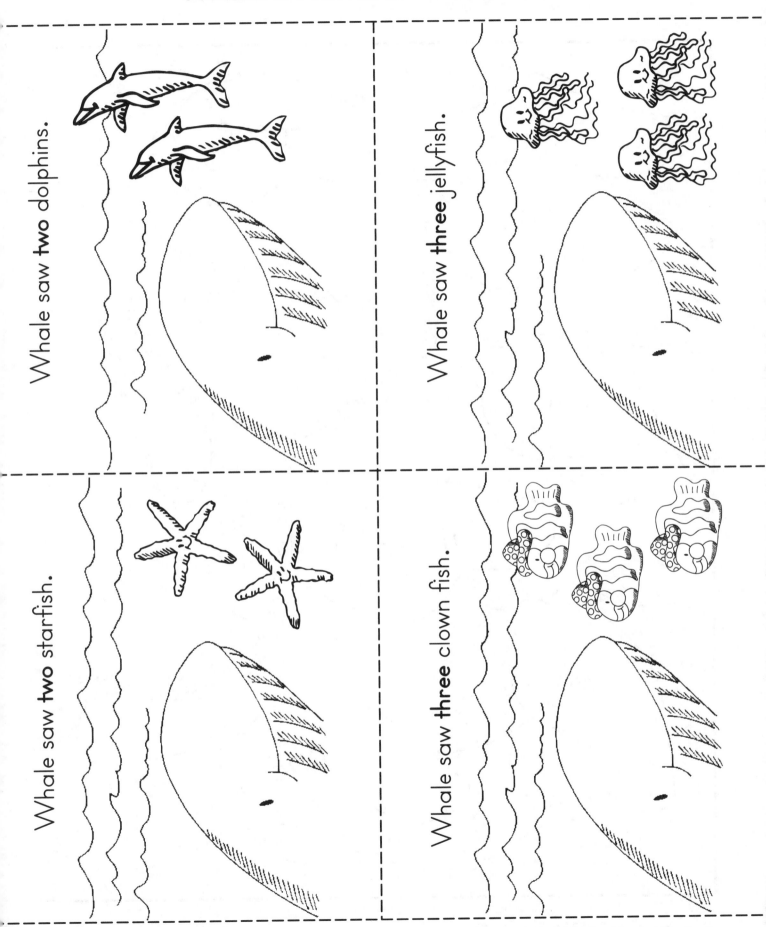

Whale saw **two** dolphins.

Whale saw **three** jellyfish.

Whale saw **two** starfish.

Whale saw **three** clown fish.

# Match Whale's Whistles

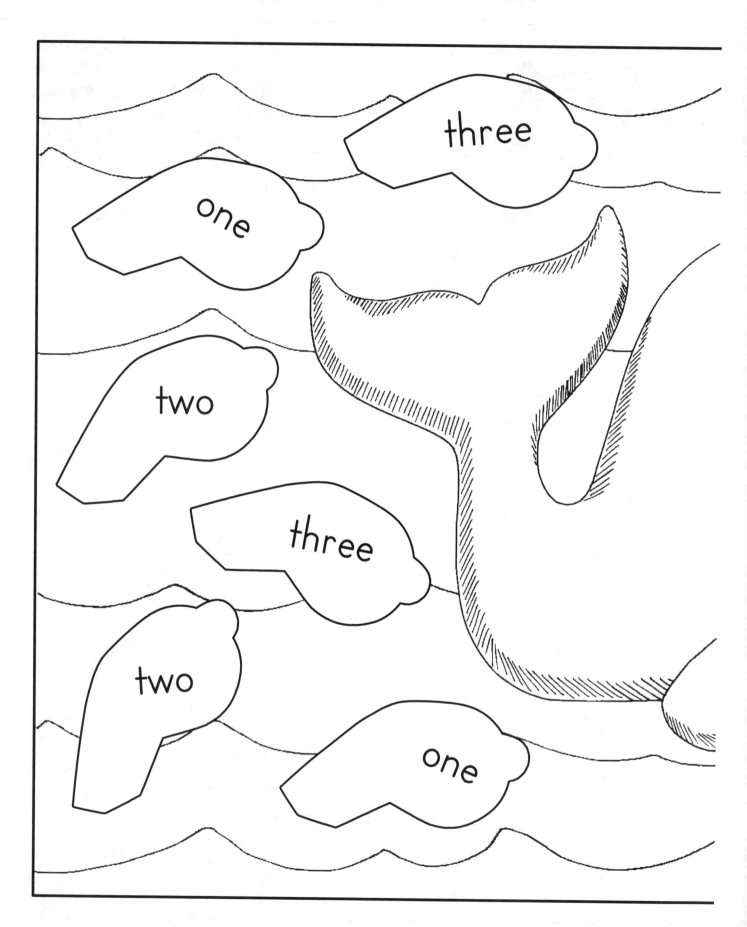

52

# Match Whale's Whistles

one

two

one

Place a matching whistle on each number word.

three

three

two

53

# Match Whale's Whistles

Reproduce, color, and cut out the whistles.

54

# Whale Puppets and Labels

Reproduce, color, and cut out twelve whale puppets. Program each whale with a number from one to twelve. Glue a craft stick to the back of each puppet. Place the puppets in numerical order.

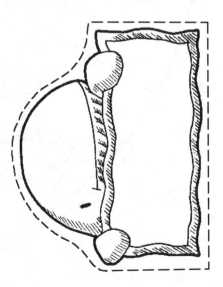

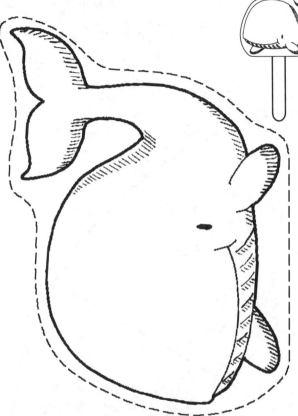

- Reproduce, color, and cut out the labels. Program and tape the labels on storage envelopes, boxes, folders, or drawers.
- Reproduce, color, and program twelve labels with numbers one to twelve. Sort and place the labels in numerical order.

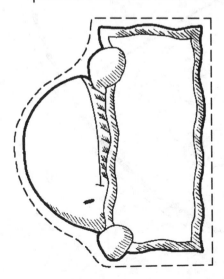
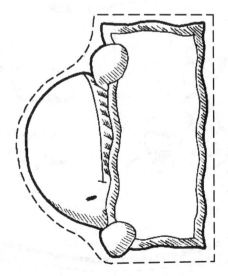
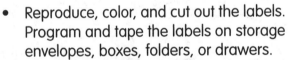

# Match Clown Fish Number Words 4-6

Reproduce, color, and cut out the match board.

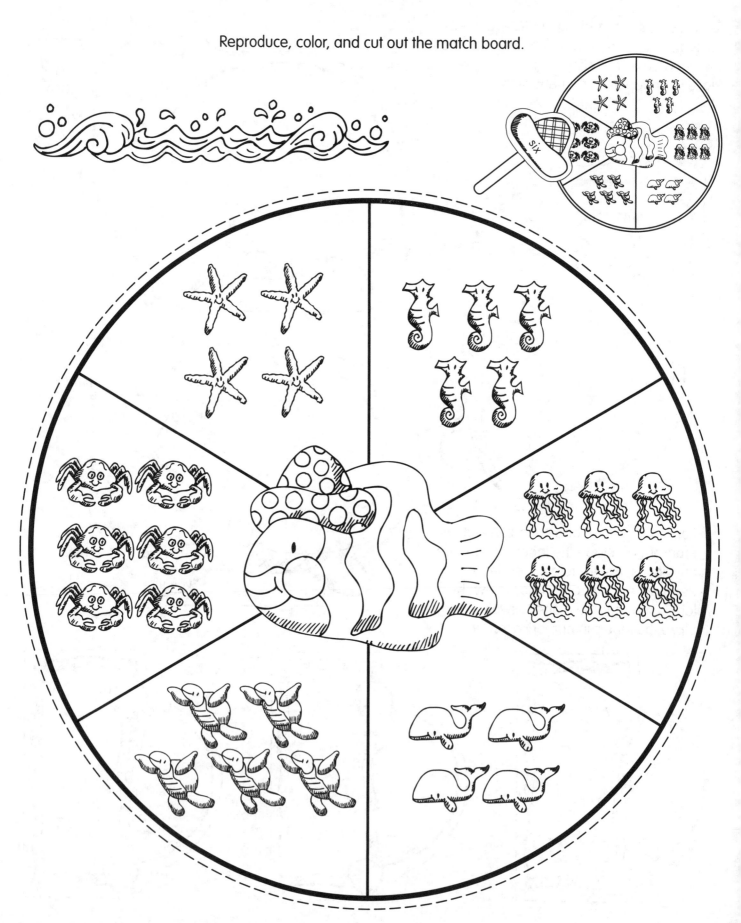

56

# Match Clown Fish Number Words 4-6

Reproduce, color, cut out, and glue a clothespin to the back of each hat.

57

# Clown Fish's Tracing Board

Look at the number words.
Trace the number words.
Color the matching number of dots.

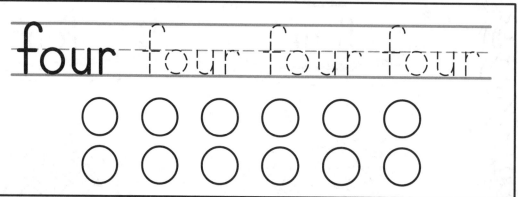

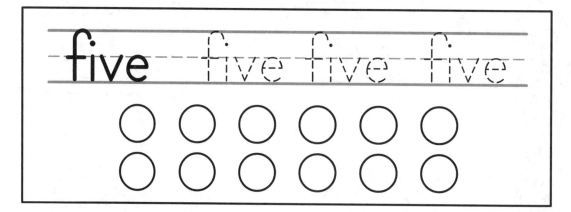

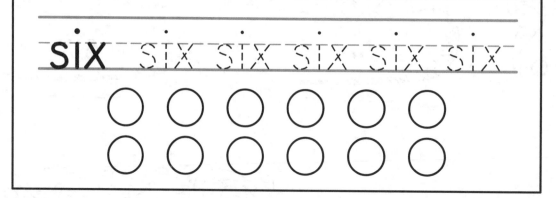

58

# Clown Fish's Writing Board

Look at the number words. Write the number words. Color the picture.

four

five

six

59

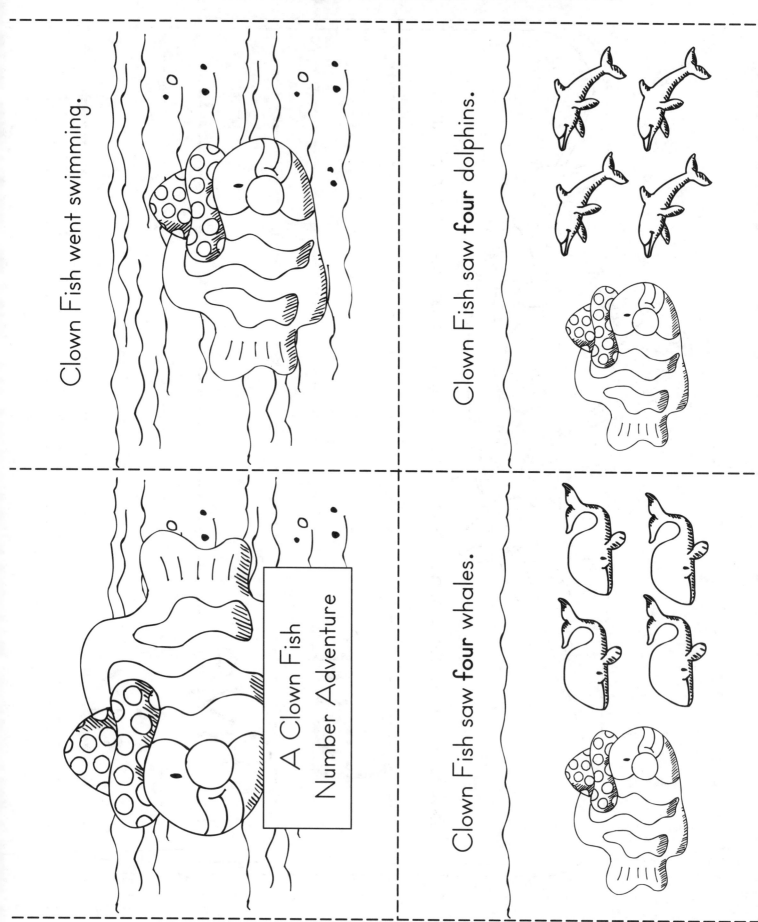

Clown Fish went swimming.

Clown Fish saw four dolphins.

A Clown Fish Number Adventure

Clown Fish saw four whales.

60

# A Clown Fish Number Adventure

Clown Fish saw **five** sea turtles.

Clown Fish saw **six** sea horses.

Clown Fish saw **five** crabs.

Clown Fish saw **six** starfish.

61

# Match Clown Fish Balloons

Place a matching number word on each balloon.

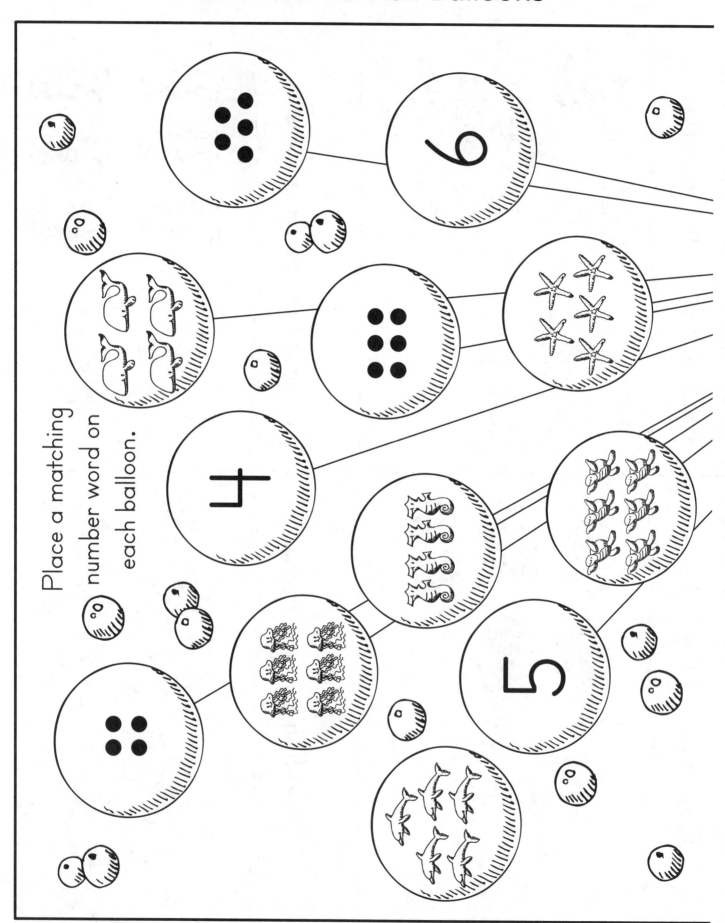

62

# Match Clown Fish Balloons

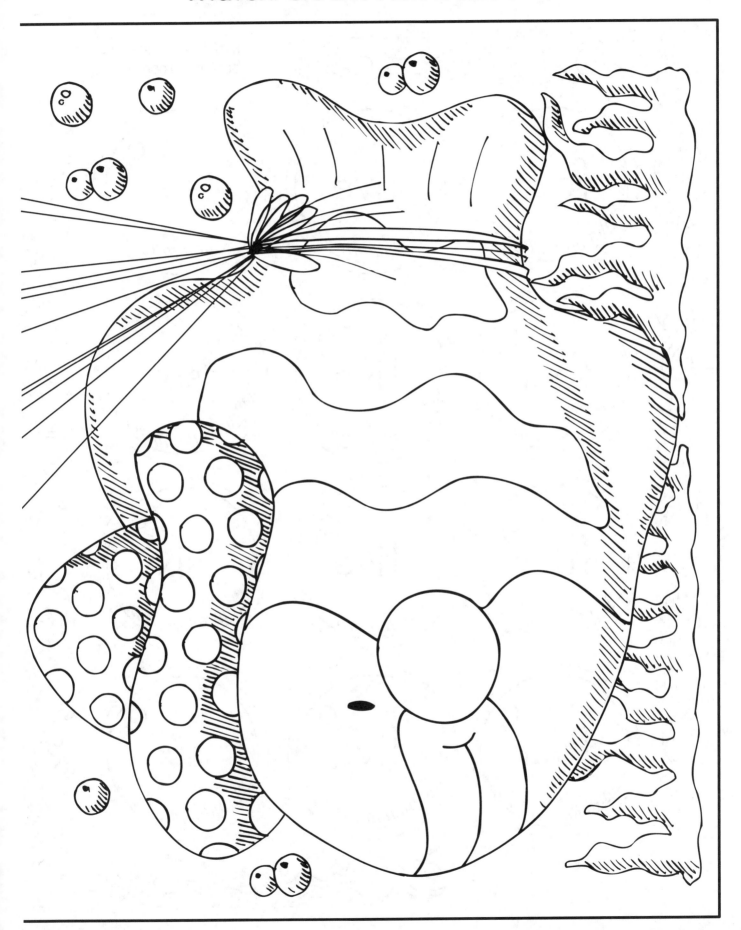

# Match Clown Fish Balloons

Reproduce, color, and cut out the balloons.

# Clown Fish Puppets and Labels

Reproduce, color, and cut out twelve clown fish puppets. Program each clown fish with a number from one to twelve. Glue a craft stick to the back of each puppet. Place the puppets in numerical order.

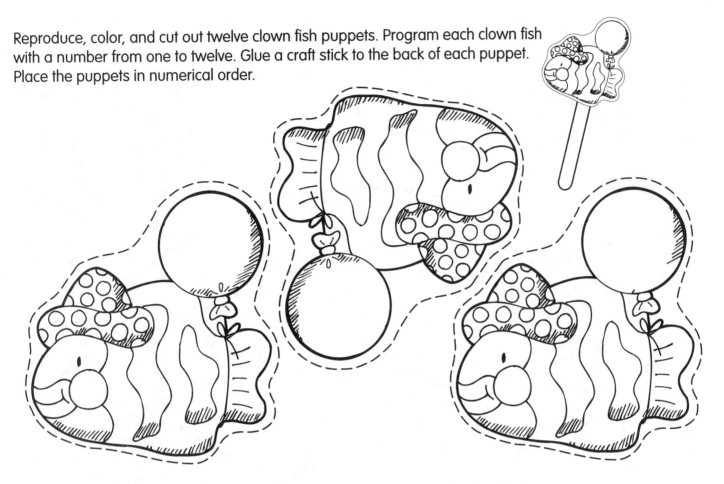

- Reproduce, color, and cut out the labels. Program and tape the labels on storage envelopes, boxes, folders, or drawers.
- Reproduce, color, and program twelve labels with numbers one to twelve. Sort and place the labels in numerical order.

65

# Match Penguin Number Words 7-9

Reproduce, color, and cut out the match board.

Reproduce, color, cut out, and glue a clothespin to the back of each surf board.

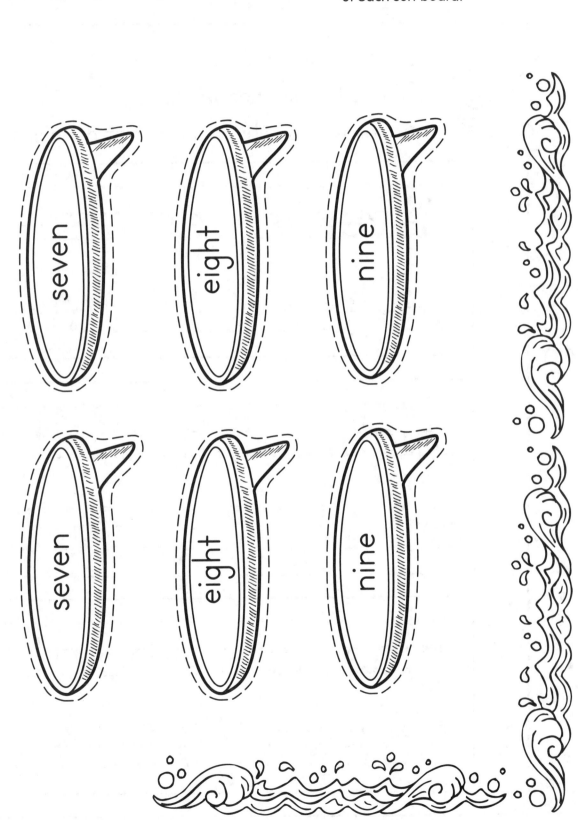

# Penguin's Tracing Board

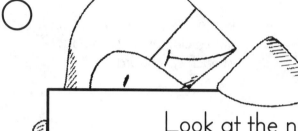

Look at the number words.
Trace the number words.
Color the matching number of penguins.

**seven** seven seven

**eight** eight eight

**nine** nine nine nine

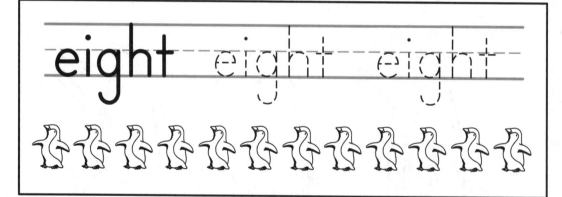

# Penguin's Writing Board

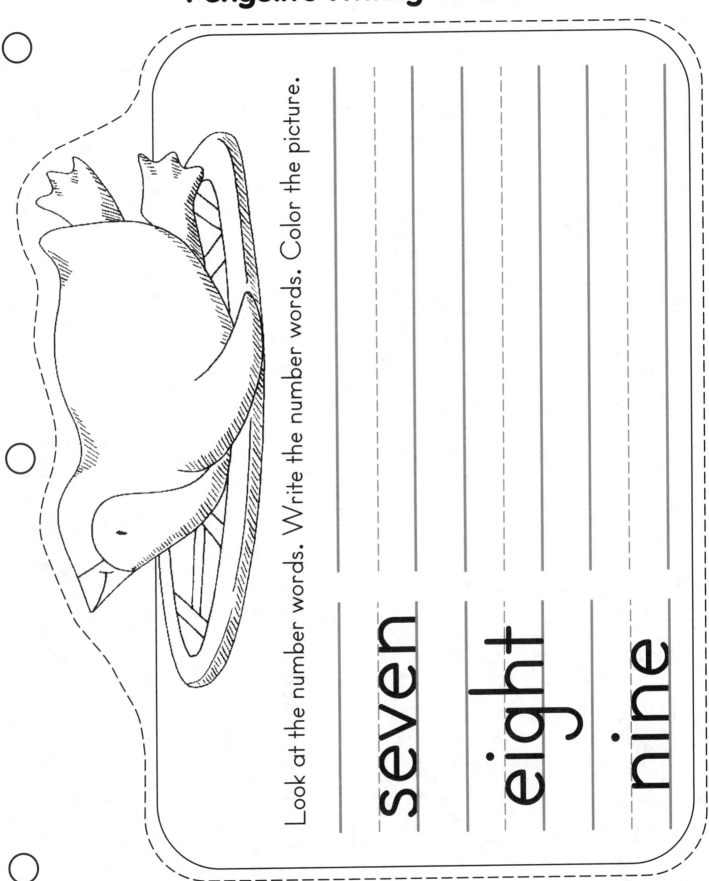

Look at the number words. Write the number words. Color the picture.

seven

eight

nine

# Penguin's Number Adventure

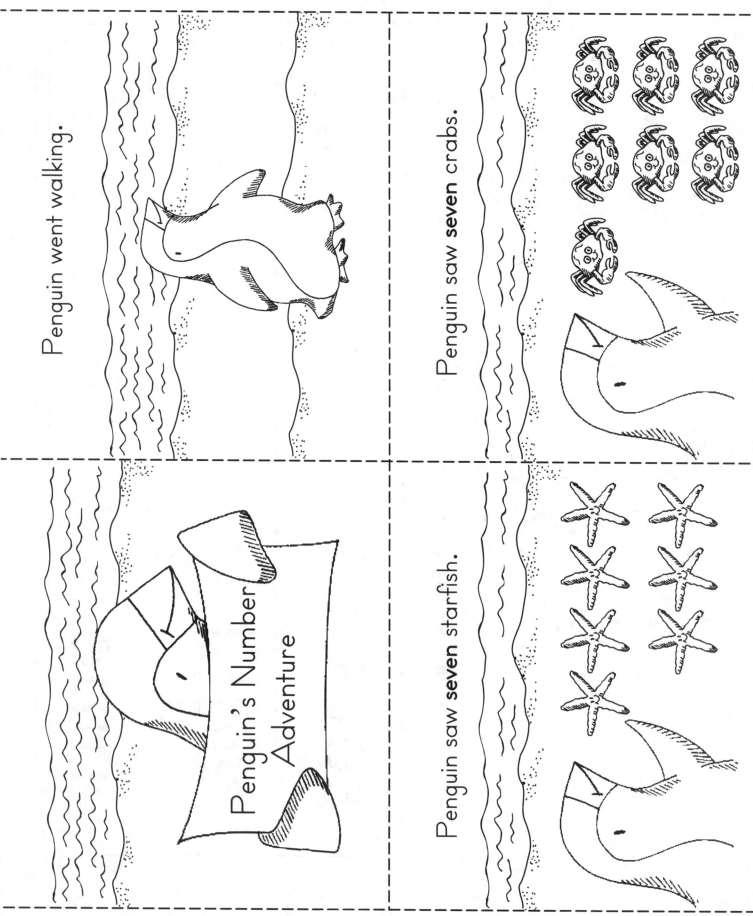

Penguin went walking.

Penguin's Number Adventure

Penguin saw **seven** crabs.

Penguin saw **seven** starfish.

70

# Penguin's Number Adventure

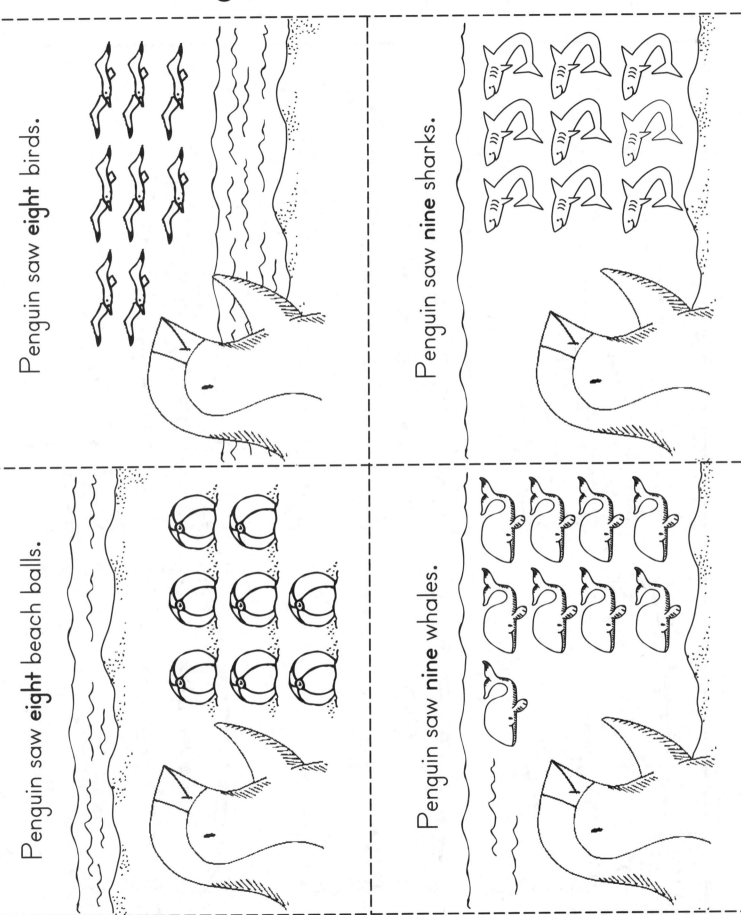

Penguin saw **eight** birds.

Penguin saw **nine** sharks.

Penguin saw **eight** beach balls.

Penguin saw **nine** whales.

71

# Surf's Up

72

# Surf's Up

Place a number word on each surf board.

73

# Surf's Up

Reproduce, color, and cut
out the surf boards.

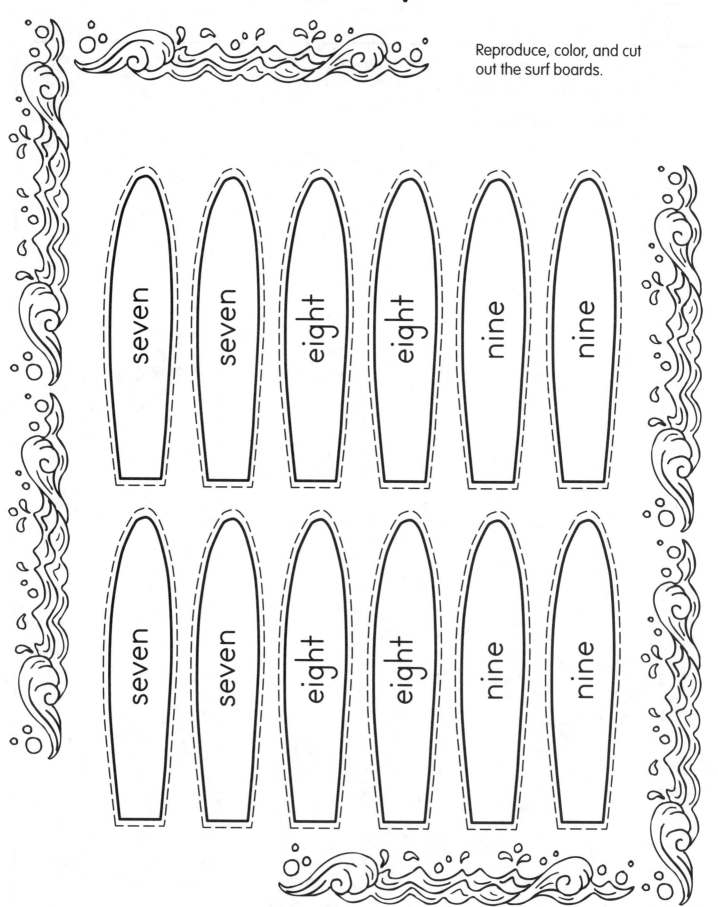

# Penguin Puppets and Labels

Reproduce, color, and cut out twelve penguin puppets. Program each penguin with a number from one to twelve. Glue a craft stick to the back of each puppet.

Place the puppets in numerical order.

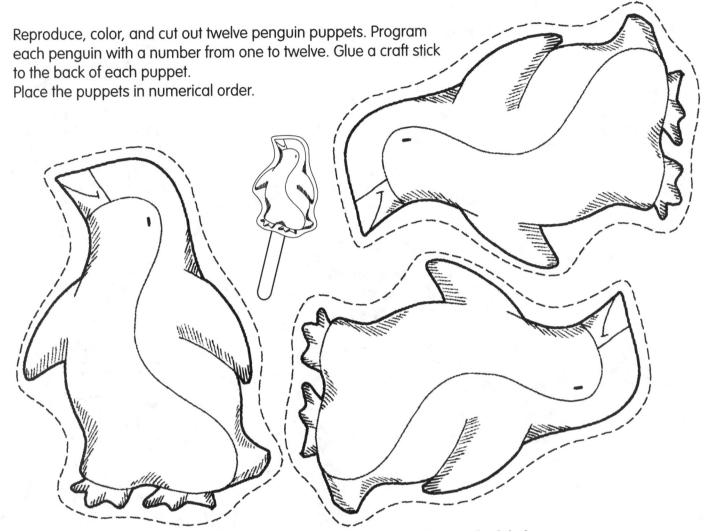

- Reproduce, color, and cut out the labels. Program and tape the labels on storage envelopes, boxes, folders, or drawers.
- Reproduce, color, and program twelve labels with numbers one to twelve. Sort and place the labels in numerical order.

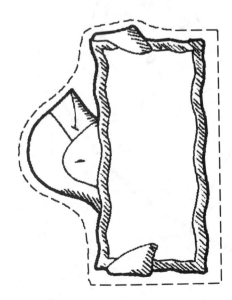 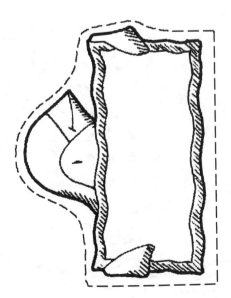 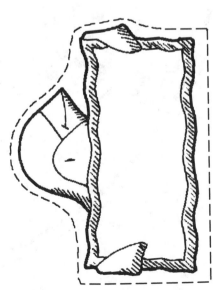

75

# Match Sea Horse Number Words 10-12

Reproduce, color, and cut out the match board.

# Match Sea Horse Number Words 10-12

Match It

Reproduce, color, cut out,
and glue a clothespin to the
back of each saddle.

# Sea Horse's Tracing Board

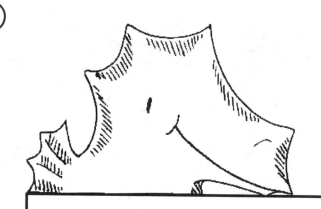

Look at the numbers.
Trace the numbers.
Color the matching number of
sea horses.

ten ~~ten ten ten ten~~

eleven ~~eleven eleven~~

twelve ~~twelve twelve~~

# Sea Horse's Writing Board

Look at the number words.
Write the number words.
Color the picture.

ten

eleven

twelve

79

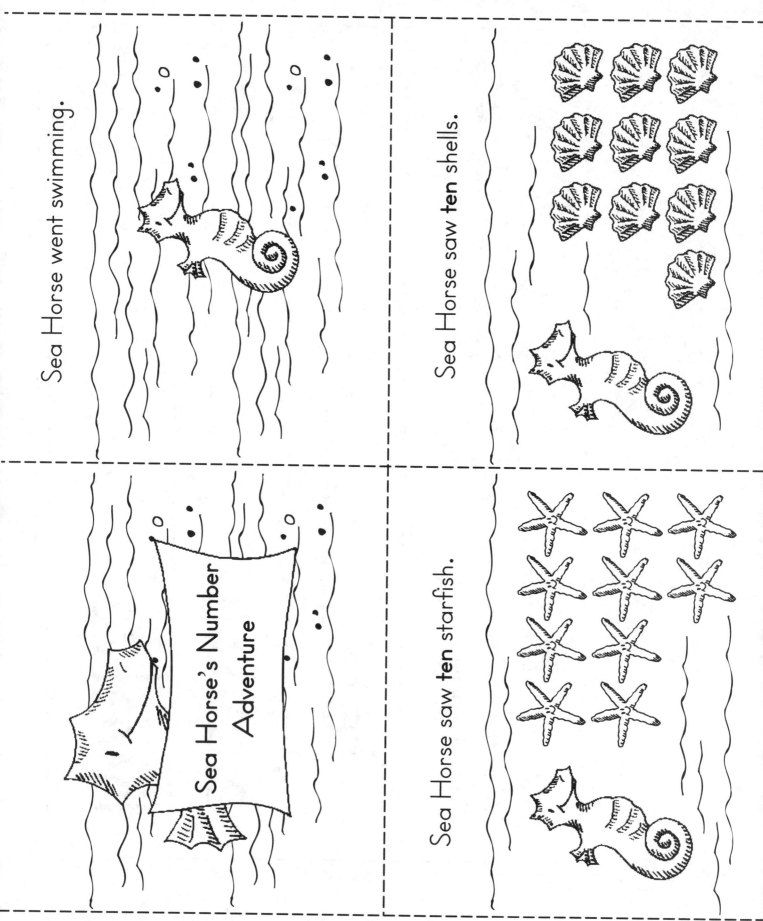

Sea Horse went swimming.

Sea Horse saw ten shells.

Sea Horse's Number Adventure

Sea Horse saw ten starfish.

80

# Sea Horse's Number Adventure

Sea Horse saw **eleven** dolphins.

Sea Horse saw **twelve** crabs.

Sea Horse saw **eleven** clown fish.

Sea Horse saw **twelve** sea turtles.

81

# Match the Saddles

Place a matching saddle on each number word.

# Match the Saddles

# Match the Saddles

Reproduce, color, and cut out the saddles.

# Sea Horse Puppets and Labels

Reproduce, color, and cut out twelve sea horse puppets. Program each sea horse with a number from one to twelve. Glue a craft stick to the back of each puppet. Place the puppets in numerical order.

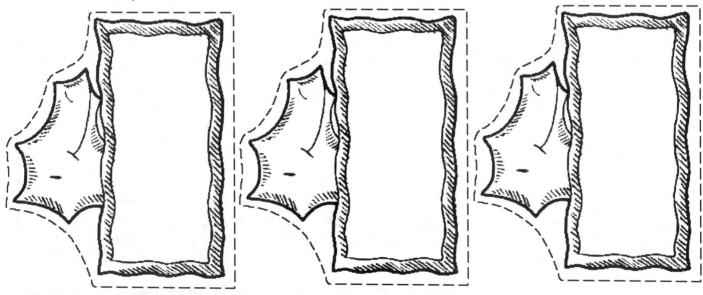

- Reproduce, color, and cut out the labels. Program and tape the labels on storage envelopes, boxes, folders, or drawers.
- Reproduce, color, and program twelve labels with numbers one to twelve. Sort and place the labels in numerical order.

85

# Number of the Day
## Flip Chart

# Number of the Day Flip Chart Page

# Numerals Borders

88

# Numerals Borders

# Numerals Borders

90

# Number Words Borders

one two three four

one two three four

# Number Words Borders

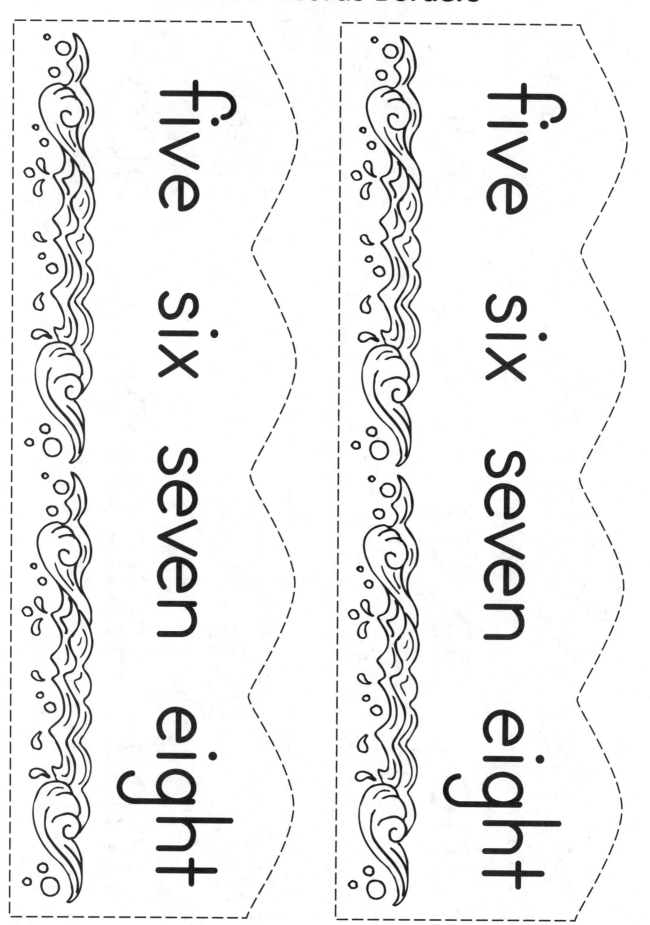

# Number Words Borders

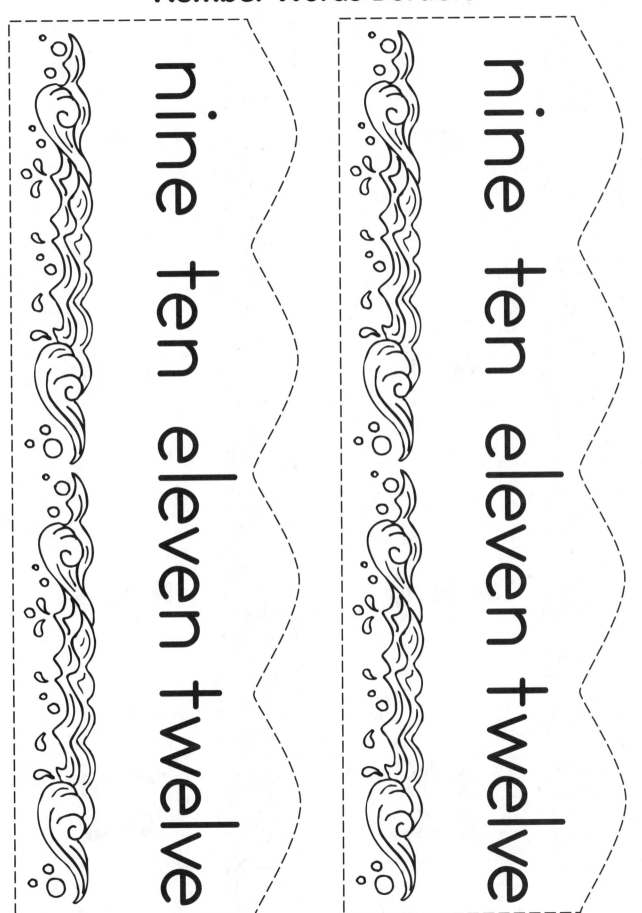

# Number Sets Borders

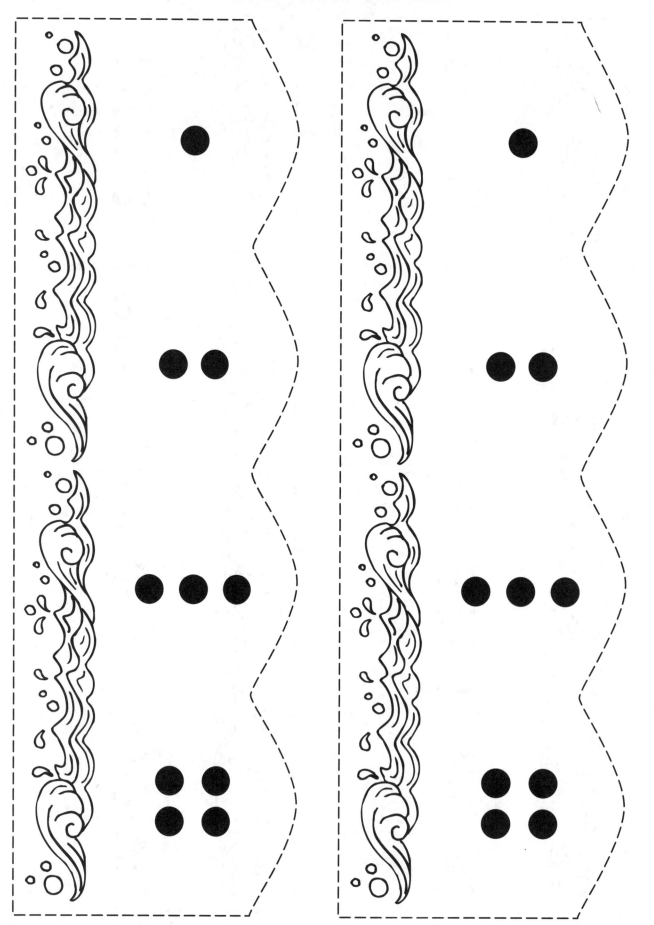

# Number Sets Borders

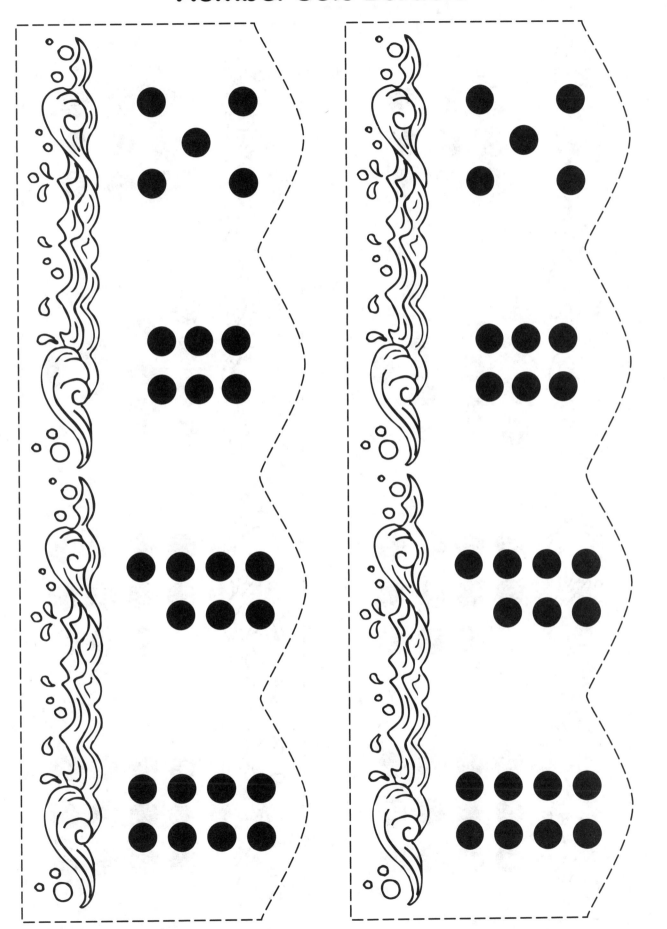

95

# Number Sets Borders

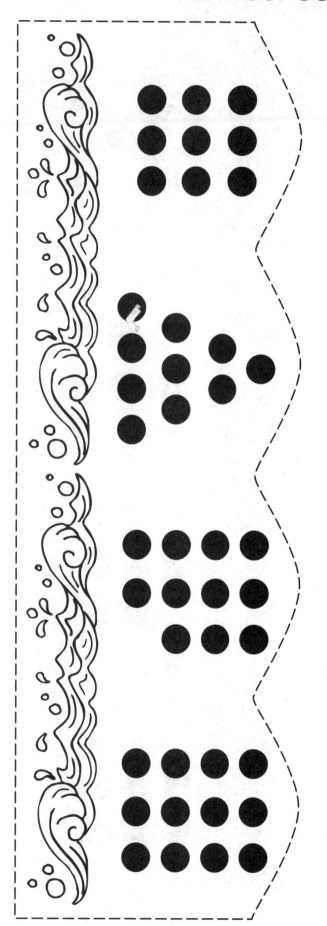

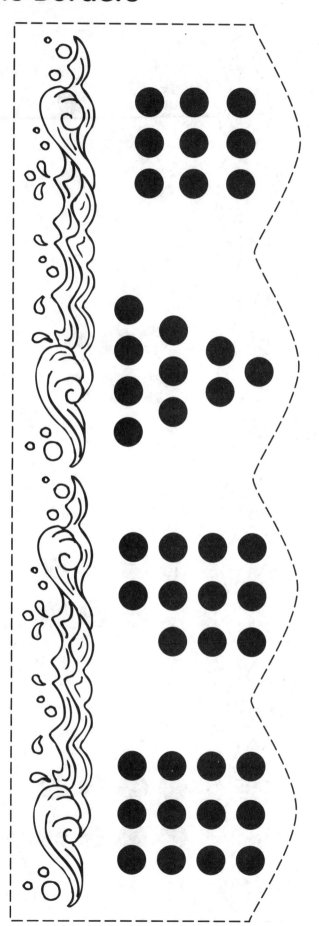

96